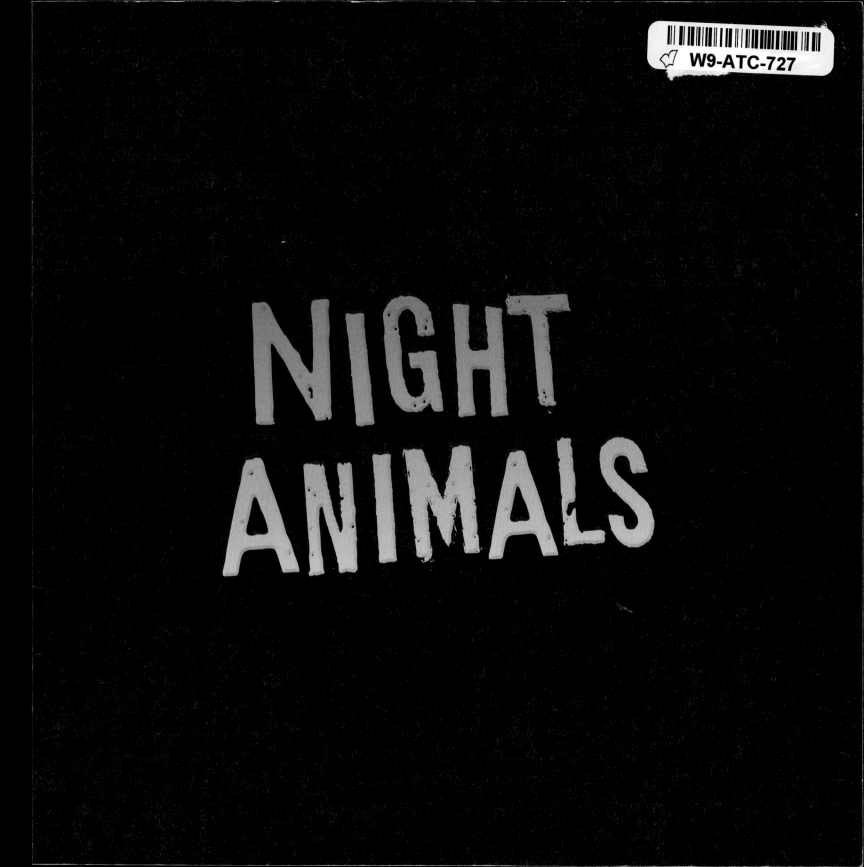

NIGHT ANIMALS

Gianna Marino

SCHOLASTIC INC.

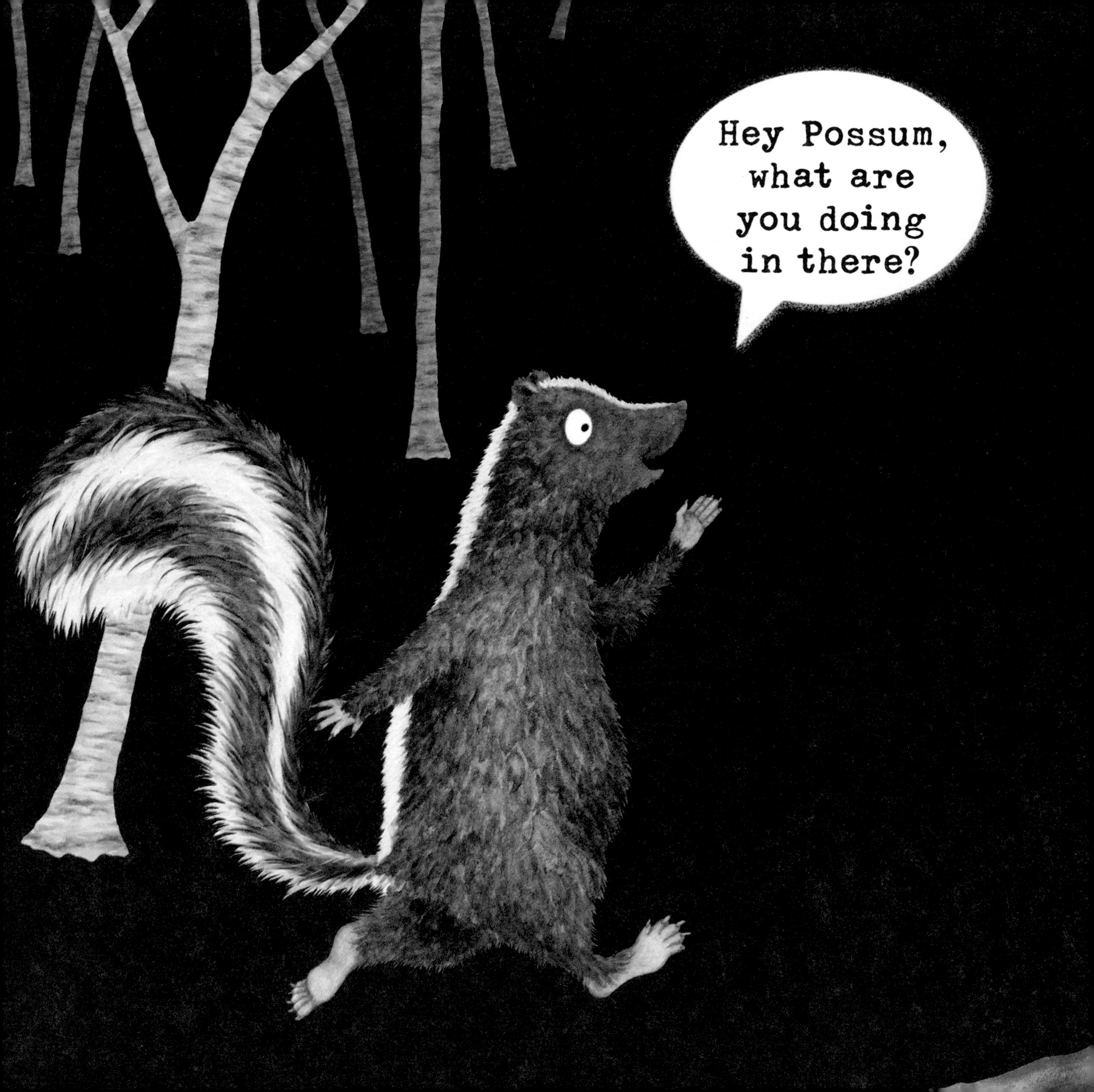
Hey Possum, what are you doing in there?

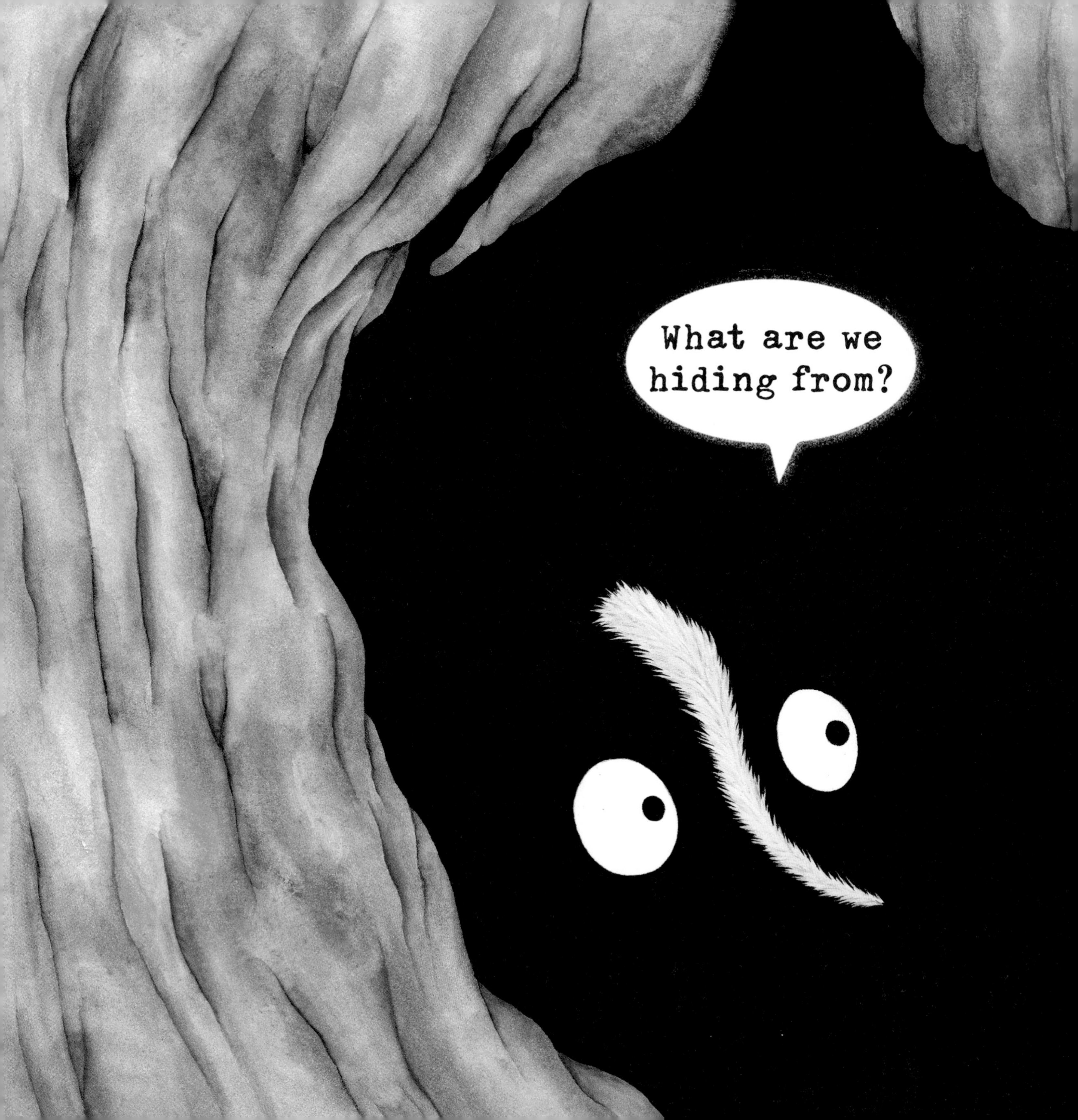
What are we hiding from?

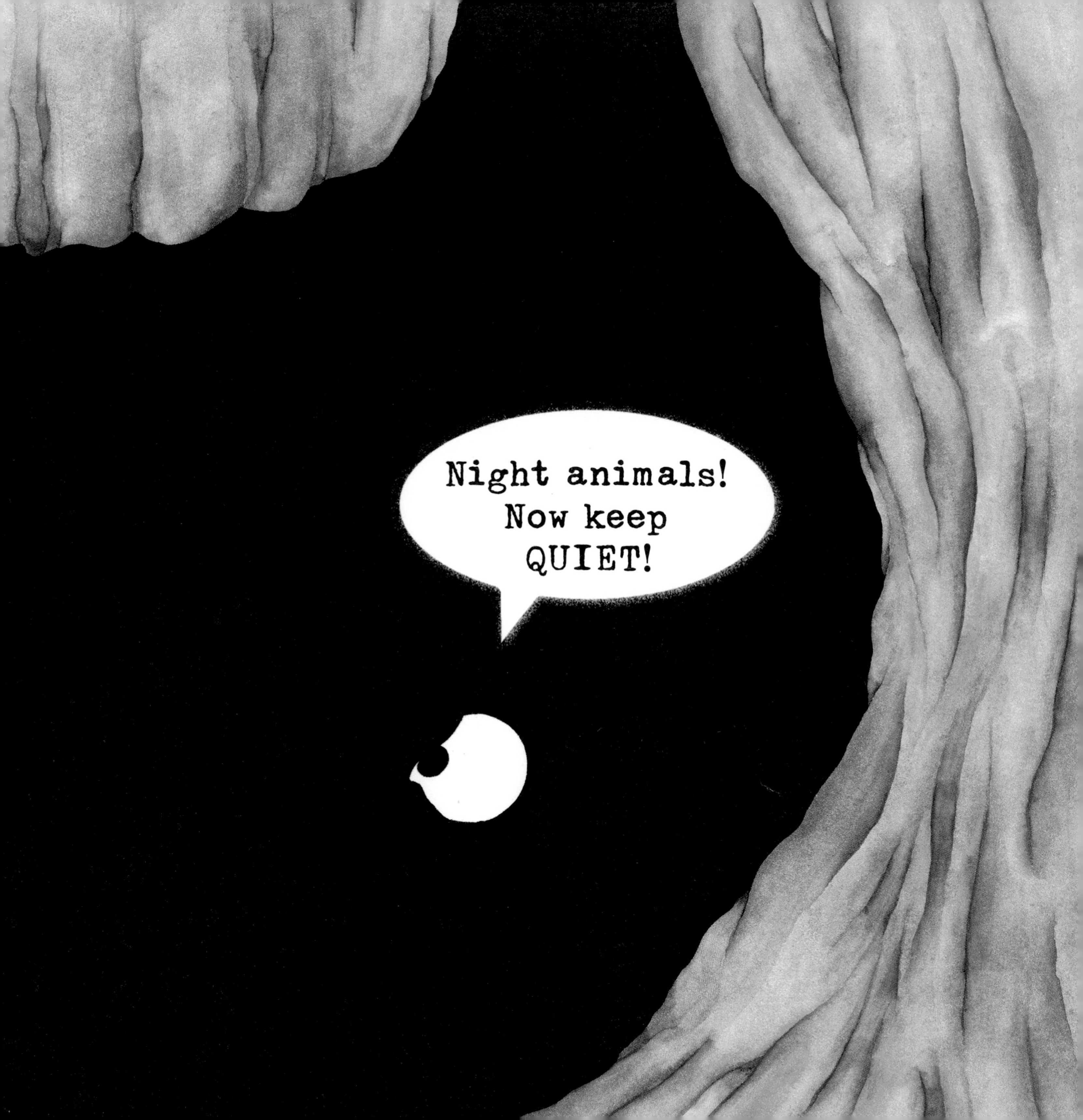
Night animals! Now keep QUIET!

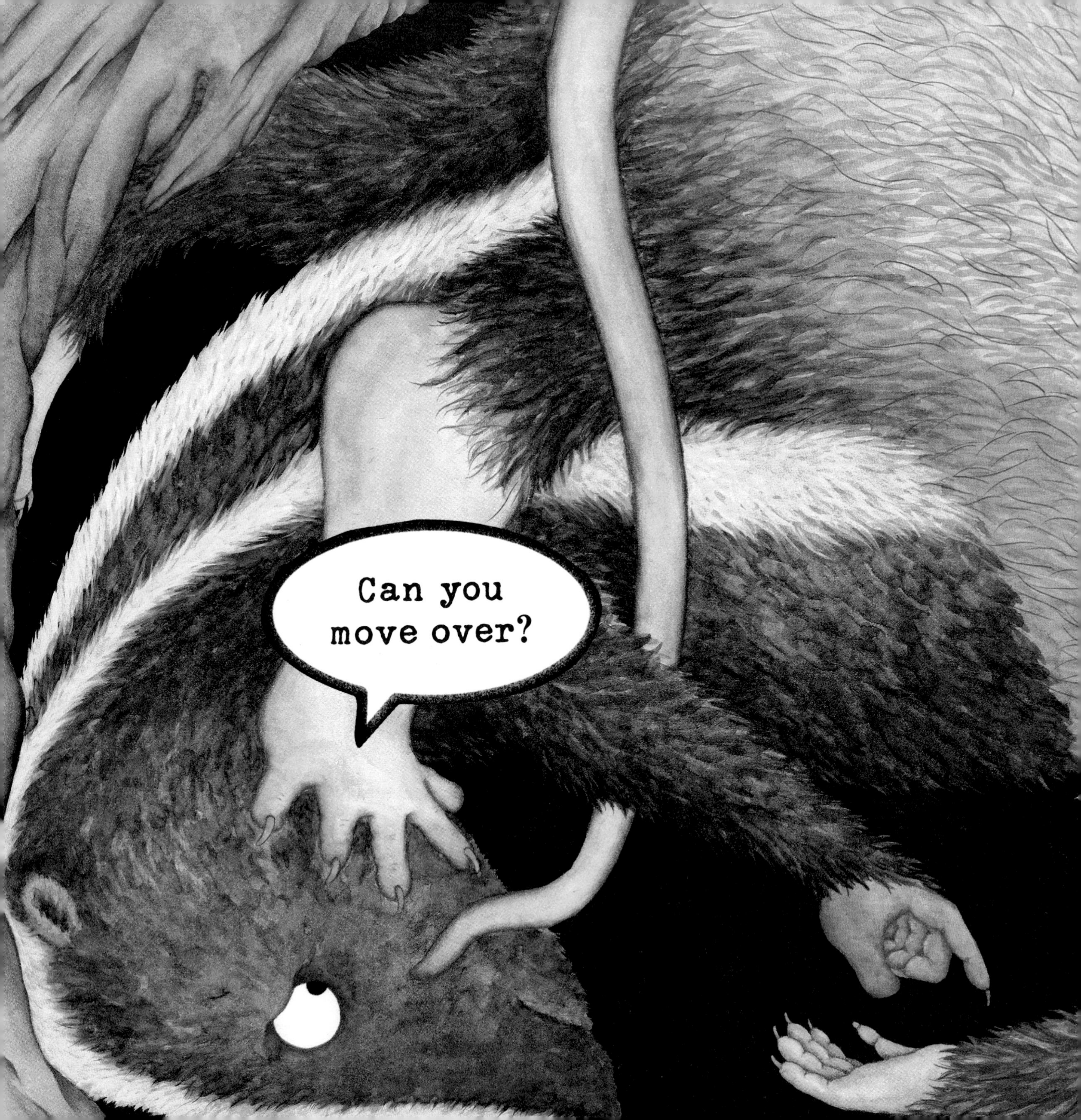
Can you
move over?

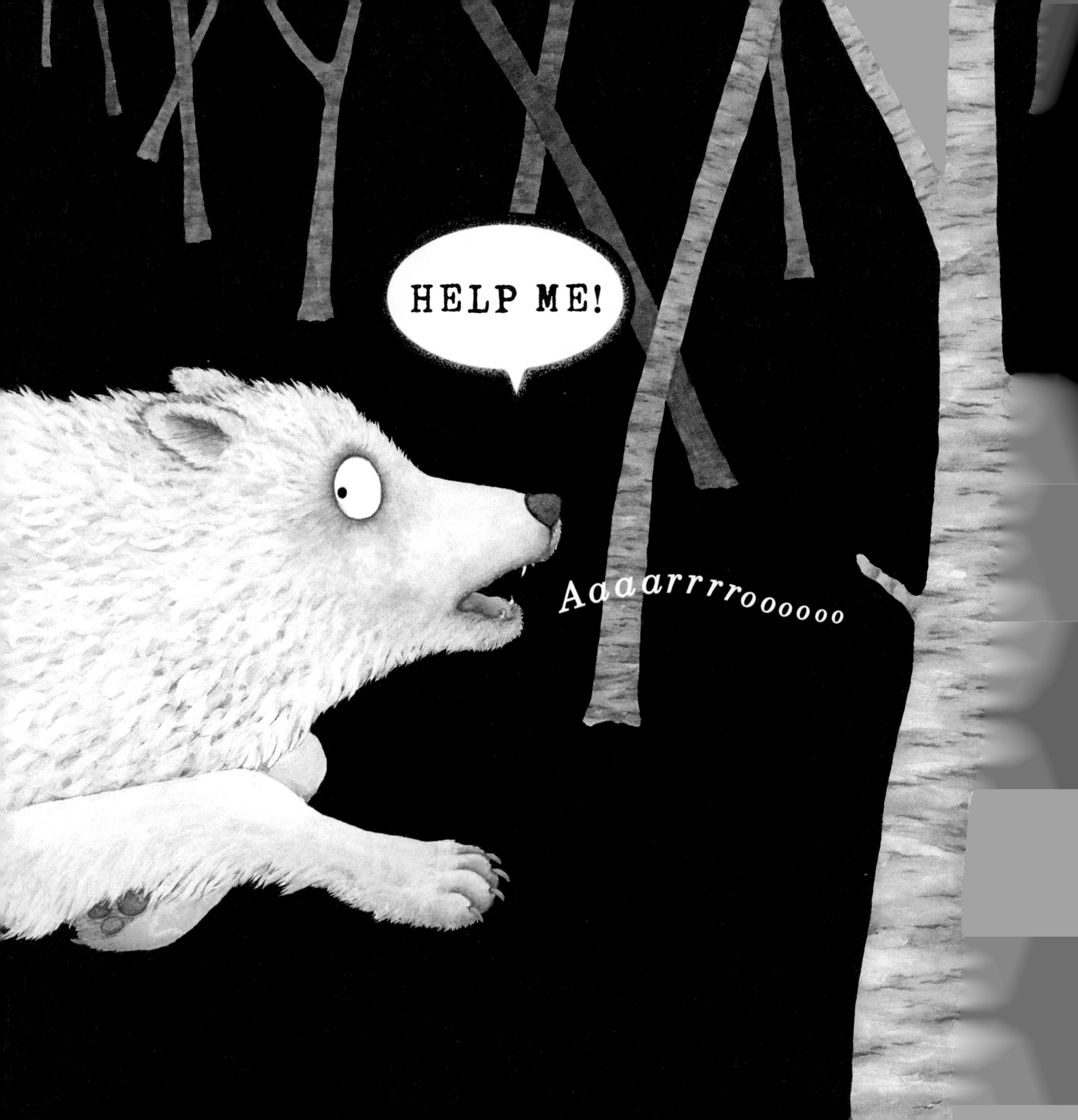
HELP ME!
Aaaarrrrooooooo

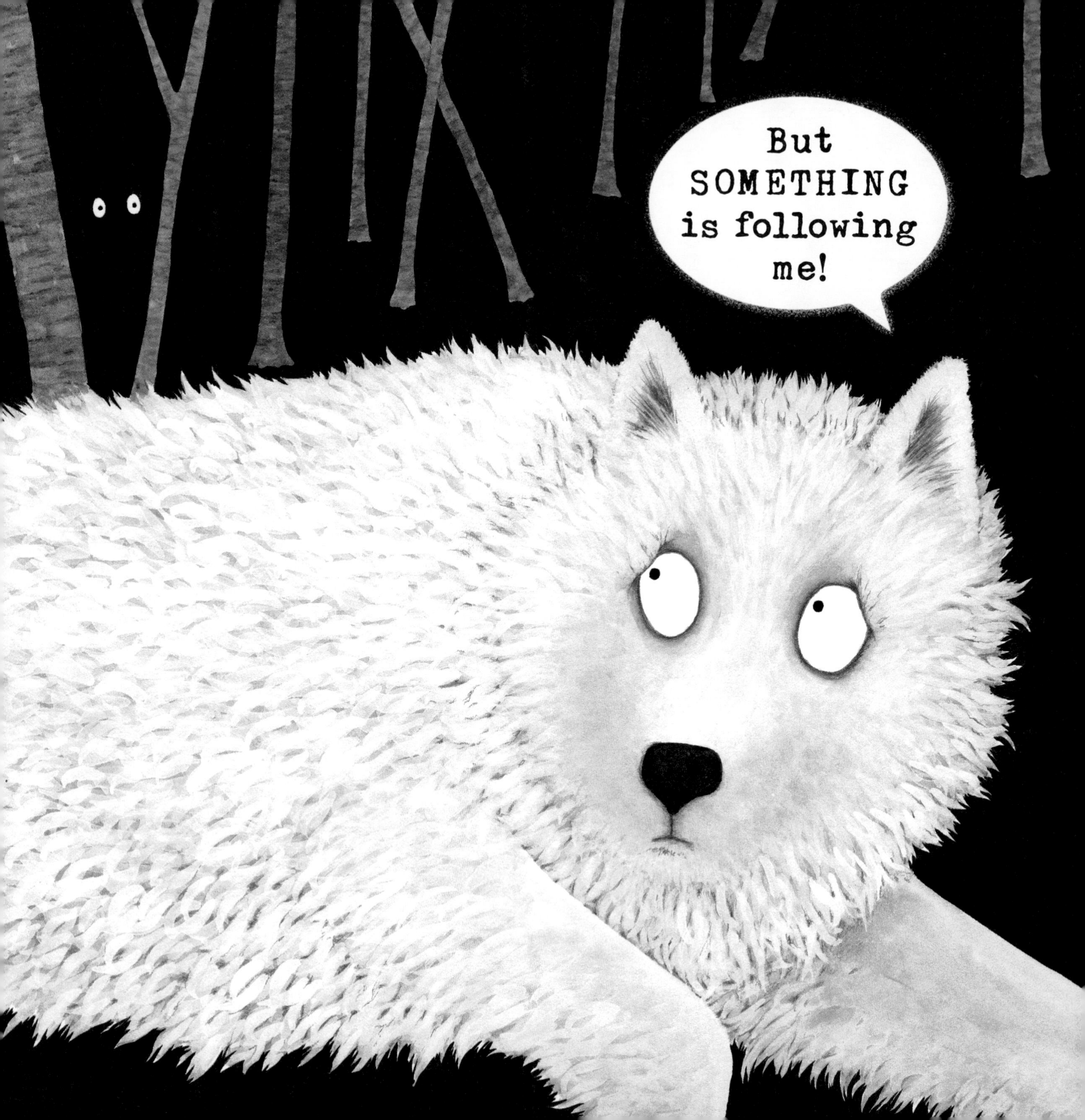
But SOMETHING is following me!

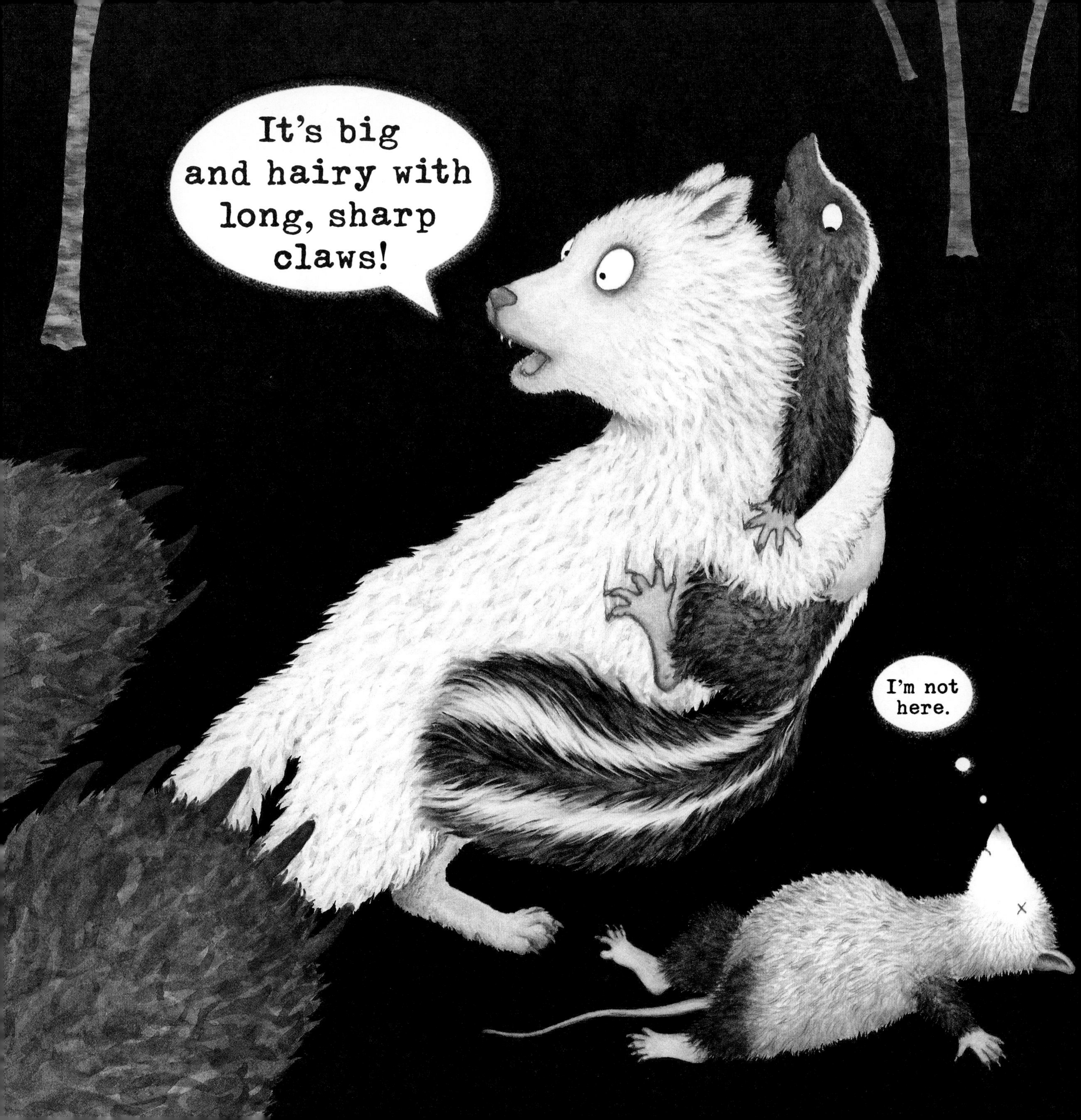
It's big and hairy with long, sharp claws!
I'm not here.

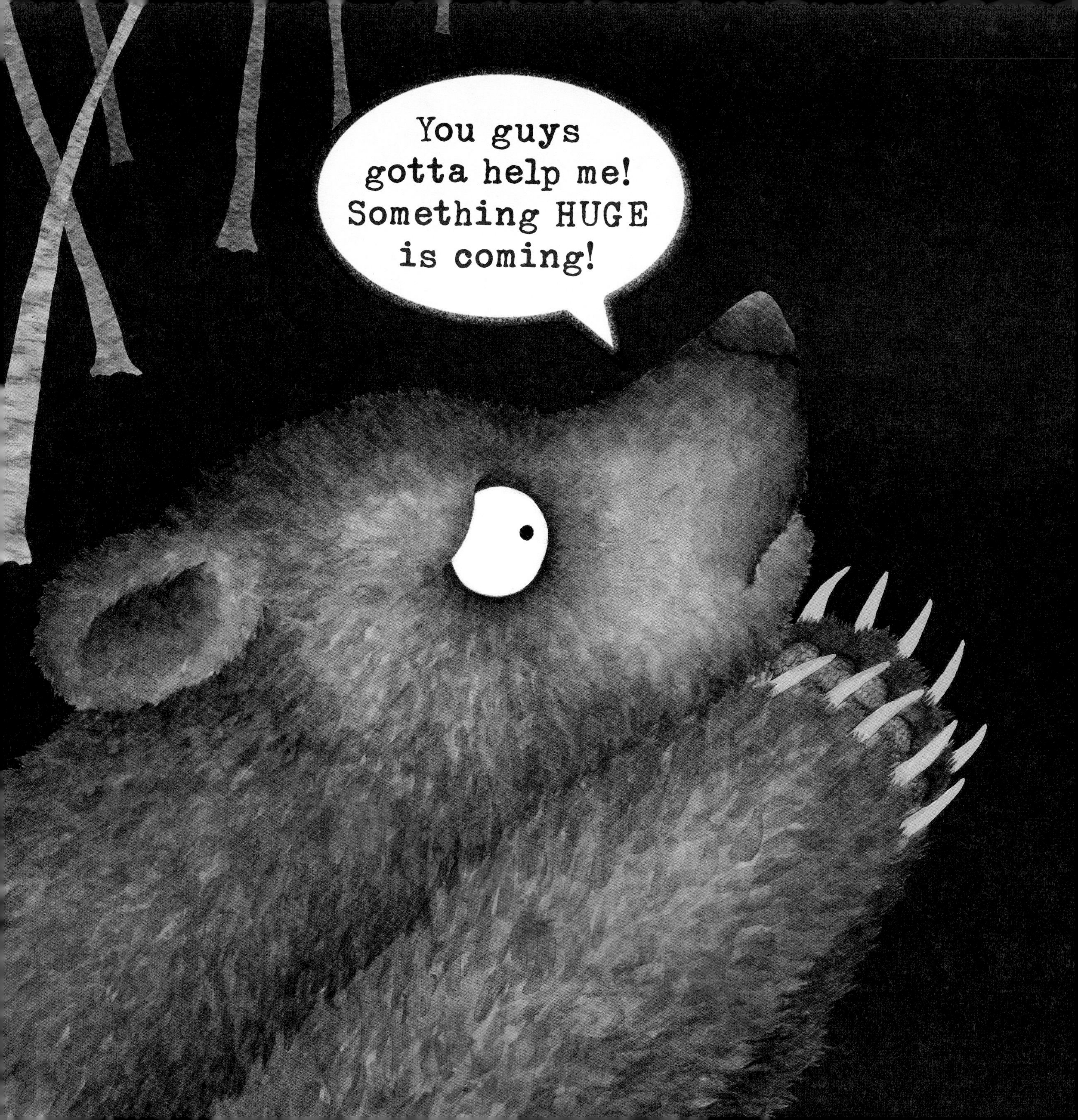
You guys gotta help me! Something HUGE is coming!

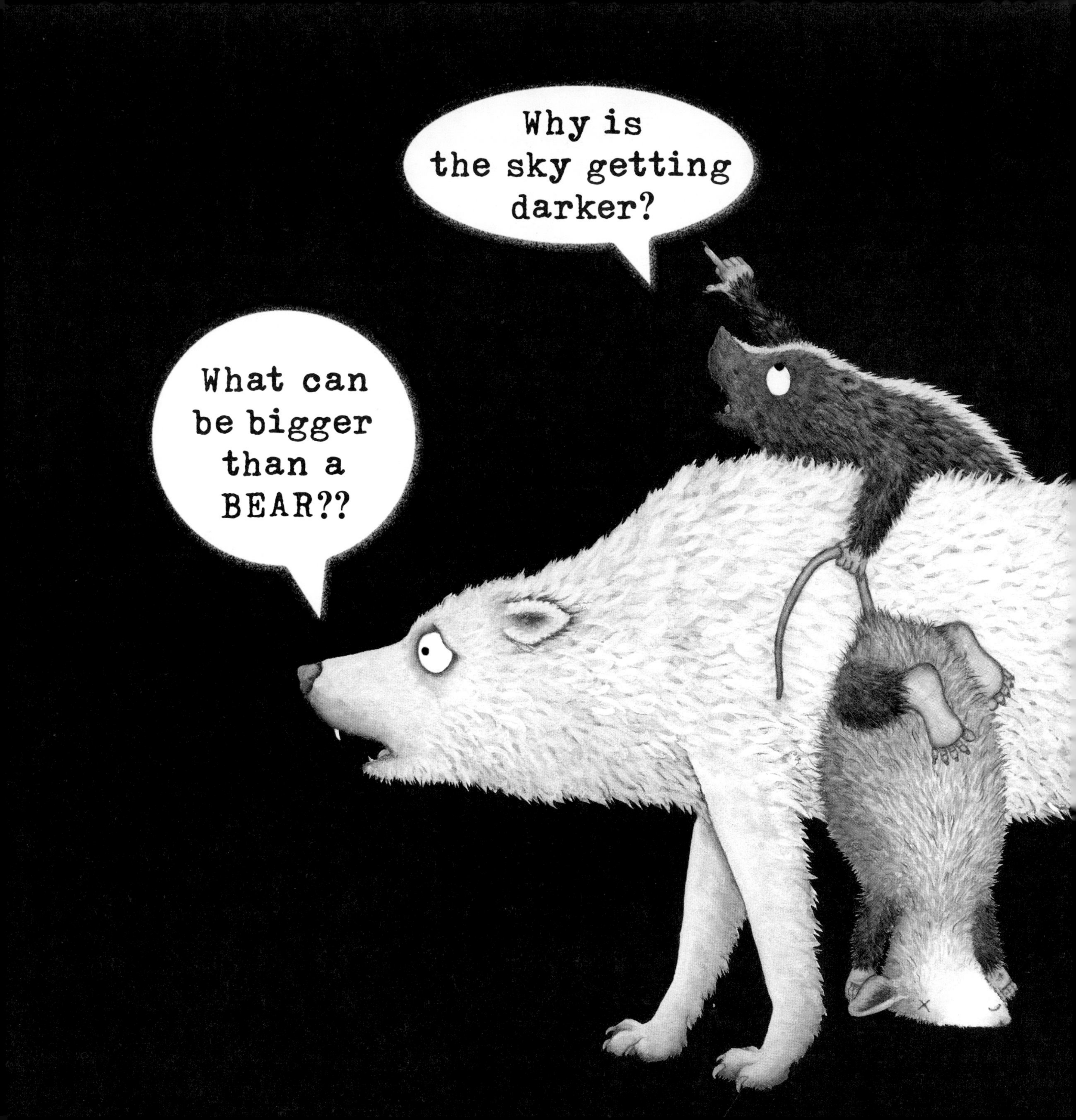
Why is the sky getting darker?
What can be bigger than a BEAR??

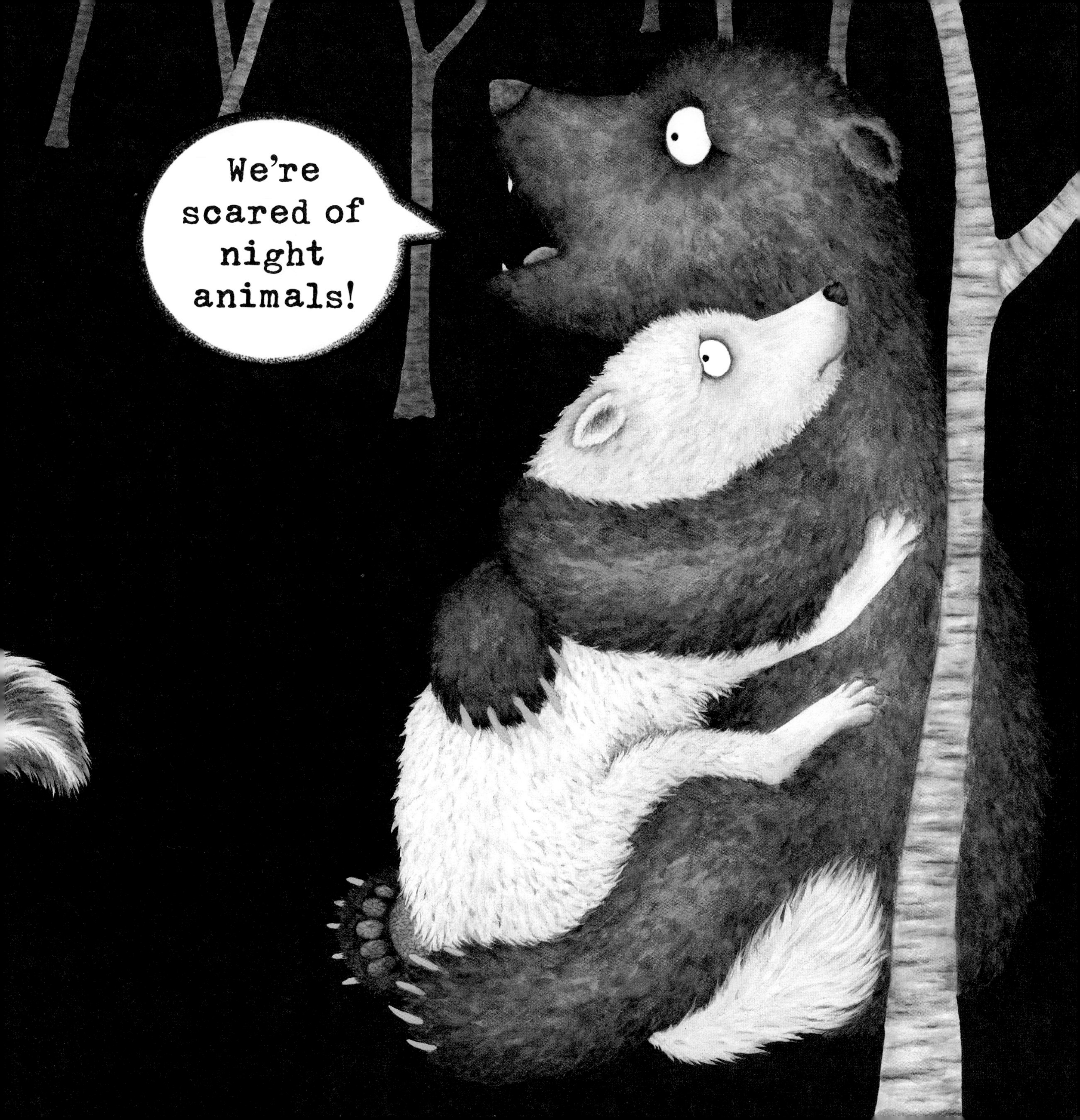
We're scared of night animals!

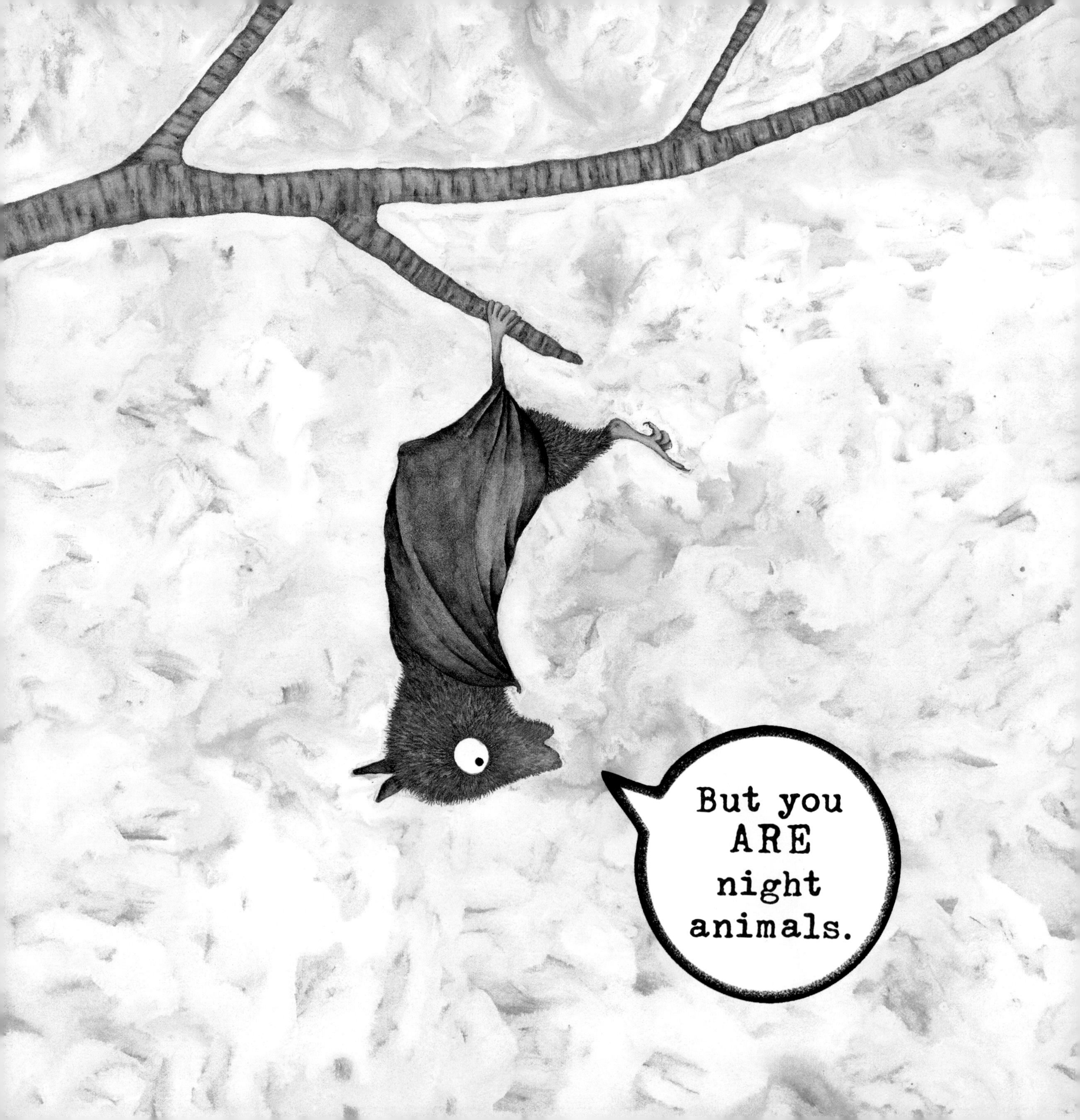
But you ARE night animals.

Click

For the Revisionaries—
Jim, Karen, Lynn, Maria, Arree, and Yuyi.
You make the dark a little less scary.

ISBN 978-1-338-05218-3

12 11 10 9 8 7 6 5 4 3 2   16 17 18 19 20 21

Printed in the U.S.A.   40

First Scholastic printing, September 2016

Designed by Nancy Brennan
The illustrations for this book were rendered in gouache and ink on Fabriano Artistico paper.